TOM WATT

RISING STARS

Rising Stars UK Ltd.
22 Grafton Street, London W1S 4EX
www.risingstars-uk.com

Text, design and layout © 2009 Rising Stars Uk Ltd.
The right of Tom Watt to be identified as the author of this work has been
asserted by him in accordance with the Copyright, Design and Patents Act,
1988.

Published 2009

Publisher: Gill Budgell
Editor: Jane Wood
Text design and typesetting: Clive Sutherland
Illustrator: Michael Emmerson for Advocate Art
Cover design: Burville-Riley Partnership
Cover photograph: Ron Co
With special thanks to; Rob
McKenzie, Kobina Crankso

British Library Cataloguing in Publication Data.
A CIP record for this book is available from the British Library.

ISBN: 978-1-84680-479-3

Printed in the UK by CPI Bookmarque, Croydon, CR0 4TD

Mixed Sources
Product group from well-managed
forests and other controlled sources
www.fsc.org   Cert no. TT-COC-002227
© 1996 Forest Stewardship Council

Contents

Map

Jeffers

Chudl

Middleton School

The Burton Twins

Nev

Kilderton

Fozzer

The Rec

Meet the Jags

Andy

Name: Andrew Burton

Fact: He's the Jags' captain.

Loves: Spurs

FYI: The Jags may be his mates, but they'd better not forget he's the Skipper.

Burts

Name: Terry Burton

Fact: He's Andy's twin brother.

Loves: Football, football, and more football. He's football crazy!

FYI: He's a big Arsenal fan.

Dev

Name: Ryan Devlin

Fact: He's very forgetful.

Loves: Daydreaming!

FYI: He's always covered in mud and bruises.

Fozzer

Name: Hamed Foster

Fact: He can run like crazy, but he shoots like crazy too – sometimes at the wrong goal!

Loves: Telling bad jokes.

FYI: His best friend is Nev.

Keeps

Name: Jim Ward

Fact: He's the Jags' Number One goalie – whether he likes it or not!

Loves: Trying to score from his end of the pitch.

FYI: He's the tallest member of the Jags.

Jeffers

Name: Jeffrey Gilfoyle Chapman

Fact: He's the only one of the Jags who doesn't live on the Chudley Park estate.

Loves: Being in the Jags.

FYI: He's the Jags' top goal-scorer.

Nev

Name: Denton Neville

Fact: Nev is the Jags' most talented player.

Loves: Fozzer's bad jokes.

FYI: He keeps his feet on the ground and always looks out for his football crazy mates.

Mrs Burton

Name: Pam Burton

Fact: The Burton twins' mum, and a team 'mum' for all the Jags.

Loves: Sorting out her boys.

FYI: Doesn't actually like football!

Mr Ward

Name: Jack Ward

Fact: He's Jim's dad and the Jags' coach!

Loves: Going on and on, doing his team talks.

FYI: He's taking his coaching exams.

Better Late Than Never

> I was watching the Spurs match on TV, but we were losing. So, I went down to the Rec. Dev was already there.

Dev   Hiya, Andy. Where is everybody?

Andy   I don't know. My brother's gone
to watch Vale United with Keeps.
Mr Ward got them tickets.

Dev   I bet they go right behind the
dugout.

Andy   Yeah. Burts likes being close up.

Dev   I know. And how are Spurs doing?

Andy   They were 2–0 down. That's why I came out!

Dev   It's more fun playing than staying in, isn't it?

Andy Yeah, especially when we've got a game tomorrow. Let's practise some free kicks.

Andy How did you get on with washing the kit?

Dev   The kit?

Andy   Yeah. You said you'd wash it last week, didn't you?

Dev   The kit?

Andy   Dev, are you all right? You remember. You told my mum she could have a week off.

Dev	The kit?
Andy	She was so pleased. No wonder she likes you best.
Dev	Um, Andy. You'll never guess what.
Andy	What? Couldn't you get all the mud out?
Dev	No, it's not that.

Andy   Don't worry. It will be all right as long as it doesn't stink too much.

Dev   Actually, I think it stinks quite a bit. I think I'd better go home.

Andy   I'll come with you. You can tell me what's wrong on the way.

Lost in the Jungle!

Oh, no! Dev had forgotten all about washing the kit. It had been in his room all week.

Dev   Sorry, Andy. I should have put it in the machine as soon as I got home. But I started watching this film on telly and I forgot.

Andy   Was it that cowboy film? It was good, wasn't it?

Dev   No, it was one where they get lost in a jungle.

Andy   Aaagh! It smells like a jungle in here. I'm going to be sick.

Dev   Yeah. Sorry if it's a bit smelly in here.

Andy   A *bit* smelly? How can you sleep in here?

Dev   I must have got used to it.

Andy   But what does your mum say?

Dev   She says she won't come in here until I've tidied up. So I left it all messy on purpose.

Andy   Did you leave the kit messy on purpose too? To keep your mum out of your room?

Dev   No. I just didn't notice it, because of all the mess. I just put it down and it's still there.

Andy   Yeah. And we've got a game tomorrow. Mr Ward won't let us wear it like that. You know he likes us to look all clean and tidy.

Dev   And what about your mum?
            She'll go mad, won't she?

Andy   She'll probably think it's funny.
            But *she* won't have to wear it,
            will she?

Dev   No. *We* will. What do you think, Andy? Maybe we won't notice the stink when we're running around.

Andy   I know the Jags, Dev. When they see that kit, they won't be running around in it. They will be running away from it!

Mum's the Word

Maybe it wasn't too late. Dev said he would tidy up his room if his mum would let him use the washing machine.

Dev   It shouldn't take too long. It's a new machine. The old one packed up last month.

Andy   Why? What did you put in it?

Dev   Um, my football boots and shin
pads. But don't tell Mum. They
were ripped to bits. And the next
day, the machine wouldn't start.

Andy   So how long will this new machine take to wash the kit?

Dev   About half an hour. Mum says this room has got to be tidy by then.

Andy   Well, you'd better get started.

Dev   I'll never do it all on my own. Can you help me?

Andy   But it's not my mess, Dev. And *you* made the deal with your mum.

Dev   But it's *our* kit, Andy. You're the skipper. You'd do anything for the Jags.

Andy   Okay, Dev. I'll help tidy up. But then we're going back to the Rec and you can go in goal so I can practise shooting.

Dev   Hmm. I suppose I'll have to!

Andy   Yes, if you want me to help you. But I'm not going near any of your smelly old socks. Look! This one's got something growing on it!

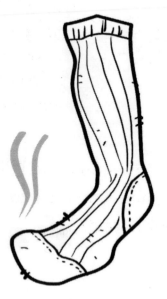

Drip Dry

We tidied Dev's room. But our problems were only just starting. The washing machine had finished ...

Dev   Just hang on a sec. When it has finished, you have to wait for the door to open.

Andy   I don't know how we tidied up that lot in your room. I just hope your mum doesn't open that cupboard. She'll get buried!

Dev   It wouldn't be the first time. Here we go. The washing is ready.

Andy   But, Dev! It's still all soaking wet!

Dev   Oh, yeah. Let's put it in the drier. There won't be time for it to dry outside. I'll put the drier on hot so it won't take long.

Dev put the soaking wet kit into the drier. He put it on hot. We went out into the garden.

Andy   It's too late to go to the Rec now, so you had better go in goal here.

Dev   But there isn't much room in the garden. Can't we do it tomorrow?

Andy   A deal is a deal, Dev. I'm David Bentley and you're in goal for Arsenal.

Dev   Hang on. That was a bit hard. You're too close!

Andy   All right, then. You throw the ball out and I'll just do headers.

Dev   Hang on. I think the drier has stopped. I'll go and look.

Andy   Dev, what is it? You look like you've just seen a ghost.

Dev   Look, Andy. Look what the drier has done to our kit! It's shrunk. It must have been too hot. What are we going to do?

Andy   What are *we* going to do? What are *you* going to do, you mean! I'd better get home and tell my mum about the kit.

Dev   All right, Andy. And if I'm not at the game tomorrow, you'll know I've left the country!

Mrs Burton
Saves the Day

Well, maybe it wasn't his fault. It was lucky that Mum had some good news when I got home. I went round to Dev's house first thing the next day.

Andy   Hello, Dev. You don't look very well. Did you get any sleep?

Dev What do you think? We've got no kit to play in and it's all my fault.

Andy There must be something we can do.

Dev What if we all play in school uniform?

Andy   No, that won't work. We go to different schools, remember? Two different school uniforms.

Dev   We could play in our own clothes.

Andy   Mr Ward won't let us do that. He'd rather call the game off.

Dev   If we can just squeeze into the kit, maybe it will stretch.

Andy   Mmm. Why don't you give it a try?

Dev   What do you think, Andy? I can
            feel it stretching a bit.

Andy   You'd need to shrink a bit as
            well, Dev! You look like you're
            wearing your little sister's t-shirt.

Dev   Then I don't know what to do. What's your mum going to say?

Andy   Funny you should ask, because I know just what she's going to say. She's going to say: "Don't worry, Dev. I know you didn't do it on purpose, which is why I'm so pleased we've had a bit of luck."

Dev   What do you mean? What bit of luck? Are you making this up?

Andy   Well, yeah. But we have had a bit of luck. Mum went in for a competition last month. And guess what? She got the first prize!

Dev   What competition? What prize? How is this going to help?

Andy   The competition was a football quiz. My brother gave her all the answers. The prize was a brand new set of football kits for a boys' team! It came yesterday!

Dev   No way!

Andy   It's true. She was going to tell us later. The Jags have got a brand new kit!

Dev   I must be dreaming.

Andy   Well, if you are, don't wake up
until we have won. The Jags will
have the best kit in Kilderton.
But we need to be the best team
as well. Get your boots. Let's go
to my house and get ready!

Dev and   Come on the Jags!
Andy

JAGUARS 1 DONSIDE 0

That was a bit of luck! We looked great in our new kit. We were playing Donside. When we put the new kit on, the Donside boys were amazed!

Andy   Thanks, Mum. This looks great. Now we'll be the smartest team around.

Dev   Not for long, Andy. Look at that pitch. It's a bit wet.

Andy   So what? If the kit gets dirty, it gets dirty. Just don't say you'll wash it again!

Dev   Here we go, ready for kick-off. Let's get it up to Jeffers so he can score.

Andy   Go on then, Dev. Your ball.

Dev   Look at Jeffers go. I'm going to get in the box.

Andy   Go on then, Dev. I'll cover for you.

Dev   Cross it, Jeffers! Yeeesss! Goal!

Andy   Great header, Dev. So that's 1–0 to the Jags. But look at all that mud. Who's going to wash that kit?

The Kit Story

When football first started, players wore long shorts and lace-up shirts. Sometimes they even wore caps to keep warm!

The first football kits were made of wool. They were itchy, and they were heavy when they got wet. Maybe that's why the game was slower then!

number

sleeve

badge

 Kits are different now. They are made of cotton or nylon. They are light. They look smart with the club badge on the front. That's why so many football fans wear them too.

 Teams now have a different kit for home and away games. Why?

The Kit Quiz

Questions

1 Why did some players wear caps in the old days?

2 Why did kits stop being made of wool?

3 Where is the club badge on a shirt?

4 What goes through the collar on a shirt?

Answers

1 To keep warm.

2 They were itchy and heavy.

3 On the front.

4 Your head!

About the Author

Tom Watt, who wrote The Jags, used to love wearing his own team's kit. It was yellow and black with *Walford Boys' Club* on it. The badge was a football wearing sunglasses! Later, the team changed their kit to black and white stripes, like the Italian team, Juventus.

Tom is a bit too old to wear a football kit now. His legs look funny in shorts these days! They always did, actually. Now, Tom only buys football kits for his son to wear when they are playing in the back garden. His son has a school kit, too. Yellow and black, just like Tom's old one.

THE JAGS

RISING★STARS

The Jags books are available from most book sellers.

**For mail order information
please call Rising Stars on 0871 47 23 01 0
or visit www.risingstars-uk.com**